the Boys' Holiday book

Buster Books

Written by Guy Campbell
Illustrated by Paul Moran
Edited by Hannah Cohen
Designed by Zoe Quayle

Cover illustrated by Nikalas Catlow
With special thanks to Hannah Thornton

First published in Great Britain in 2009 by Buster Books,
an imprint of Michael O'Mara Books Limited,
9 Lion Yard, Tremadoc Road, London SW4 7NQ

A CIP catalogue record for this book is available from the British Library.

ISBN: 978-1-906082-63-5

4 6 8 10 9 7 5

www.mombooks.com/busterbooks

Printed and bound in Italy by L.E.G.O.

CONTENTS

TRAVEL GAMES

Try out these travel games and make sure
time flies on boring journeys.

PLAY THE PACKING GAME

Take it in turns to add to a list of things
you packed in your suitcase. The first
player starts the game by saying, 'I
packed my suitcase...' and then chooses
an item to pack in it. For example, '...and
I put in a towel'.

The next person has to add another
item. So they might say, 'I packed my
suitcase and I put in a towel and an
alarm clock'.

Anyone who forgets an item while
repeating the list is out.

The game continues until only one
player remains.

CATEGORIES

Think of five categories of different
things. For example, fruits, sports,
countries, animals and boys' names.

Now pick a letter, for instance, 'B'.
Give everyone two minutes to write
down things beginning with B that
match each category – the fruit might
be a banana, the sport could be
badminton, the country could be Brazil,
the animal could be a baboon and the
boy's name could be Ben, and so on.

Each player gets one point for every
category they have filled, and two points
if they gave an answer that nobody else
got. Keep playing with new rounds and
new letters – the first person to reach
50 points, wins the game.

TWENTY QUESTIONS

One person thinks of a famous person,
place or thing, such as Napoleon, or the
North Pole, or the Statue of Liberty.
Then everybody else asks up to 20
questions to guess what it is. Warning –
the answer to the questions can only be
'Yes' or 'No'. For example, 'Are you a
person?', or 'Are you still alive?'

The first person to guess the answer
wins and then it's their turn to pick a
person, place or thing.

What can he see from the car window?

UP, UP AND AWAY

Flying is always exciting, especially the bit when the wheels leave the ground as you take off. Now, being in the airport lounge can be fun, too, with these tricky puzzles to solve. Check your answers on page 62.

DASH TO CHECK-IN

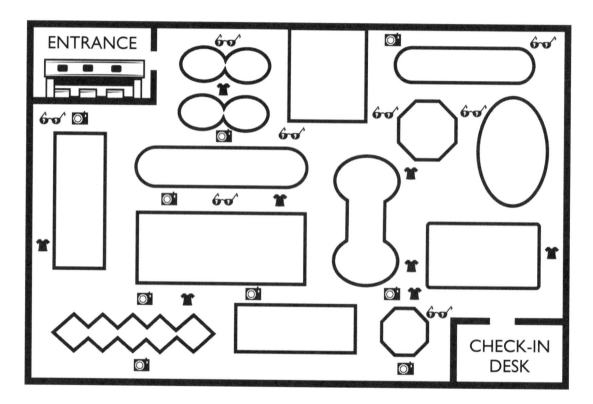

You have ten minutes to fill before getting on the plane, so you decide to visit the shops.

Can you find a path from the Entrance to the Check-in desk which means you pass over only one sunglasses symbol, one camera symbol and one T-shirt symbol? Good luck.

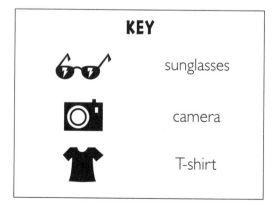

KEY

sunglasses

camera

T-shirt

What's for lunch in the sky?

CONVEYOR-BELT CHAOS

Charlie's suitcase has a luggage ticket tied to it and a round black sticker on it, but not a triangular white sticker. Can you help him find it?

WORLD FACTS QUIZ

Test out your family's knowledge of the world
with this fun fact-filled quiz. Write each player's answers – A, B, C
or D – in the scorecard on the opposite page. All the answers are on page 62.

---

1. The Eiffel Tower is a tourist attraction in which city?

A. New York
B. Beijing
C. Paris
D. Rome

---

2. In which country are you most likely to eat spaghetti?

A. Japan
B. Italy
C. India
D. Nepal

---

3. Where do kangaroos come from?

A. Singapore
B. Cambodia
C. Canada
D. Australia

---

4. Where are the Pharaohs buried?

A. The Leaning Tower of Pisa, Italy
B. The Pantheon, Greece
C. The Pyramids of Egypt
D. Buckingham Palace, England

---

5. In which country is the Taj Mahal?

A. France
B. Portugal
C. Italy
D. India

---

6. Which language do most people speak in Brazil?

A. Portuguese
B. Chinese
C. English
D. French

---

7. What are the Niagara Falls?

A. Waterfalls
B. Mountains
C. Pyramids
D. Oceans

---

8. Which of these is an animal-watching holiday in Africa?

A. A hike
B. A cruise
C. A marathon
D. A safari

---

9. What is the world's favourite ice-cream flavour?

A. Chilli
B. Pineapple
C. Lime
D. Vanilla

---

10. Which of these islands would you find in the Caribbean Sea?

A. Jamaica
B. Ireland
C. Australia
D. Iceland

---

11. What kind of money could you spend in India?

    A. Rupee
    B. Whoopee
    C. Loopee
    D. Hoopee

13. In which country do people famously eat snails?

    A. Greenland
    B. Norway
    C. France
    D. Italy

12. Which of these words means 'Hello' in Spanish?

    A. Bonjour
    B. Hola
    C. Howdy
    D. Paella

14. Which country held the Olympics in 2008?

    A. The USA
    B. Great Britain
    C. China
    D. Australia

Question	Player One	Player Two	Player Three	Player Four
1				
2				
3				
4				
5				
6				
7				
8				
9				
10				
11				
12				
13				
14				
TOTAL SCORE				

PICTURE PUZZLER

Tackle these picture puzzles. The first one is a brain-teaser, the second one is a brain-buster! Check your answers on page 62.

Complete this grid so that the four different pictures shown below appear in every row, in every column, and in each outlined block of four squares.

Fancy a harder puzzle? Have a go at completing the grid below so the nine different pictures shown at the bottom of the page appear in every row, every column and in each outlined block of nine squares. Good luck.

WORLD SPORTING CHALLENGE

Sport stars come from all over the world and this puts your sporting knowledge to the test. The answers are on page 62.

Can you match up the star with the sport that he is famous for? The first one has been done to start you off.

Cristiano Ronaldo — Athletics

Lewis Hamilton — Football

Roger Federer — Motor racing

Tiger Woods — Tennis

Sachin Tendulkar — Golf

Usain Bolt — Swimming

Ian Thorpe — Cricket

Now see if you can match the star to the country he was born in.

Cristiano Ronaldo — Great Britain

Lewis Hamilton — Jamaica

Roger Federer — Switzerland

Tiger Woods — Australia

Sachin Tendulkar — Portugal

Usain Bolt — USA

Ian Thorpe — India

PERFECT POOL GAMES

Are you bored of pool-side posing? Jump in and play these super-fun pool games and start having a seriously splashing time.

SHARK!

One player is the 'Shark' and must position himself on one side of the pool. The other players are the 'Fish' and must gather together at the other side of the pool.

The Fish must try to get to the Shark's side of the pool without the Shark tagging them. When all the Fish have either made it to the other side or have been tagged, play the game again with any captured Fish now acting as Sharks. The Fish that lasts the longest before being tagged is the winner.

MARCO POLO

This is a tag game named after the famous explorer Marco Polo, and it is played in the pool.

One player is 'Marco' and must keep his eyes closed the whole time. The other players scatter around the pool. However, whenever Marco shouts out 'Marco', all the other players must reply 'Polo'. Marco has to work out where they are from their replies, and try to 'tag' them. The last player tagged becomes the next Marco.

PEARL DIVER

For this game you need 'pearls' to throw into the pool. A pearl should be something that sinks, such as a locker key or a small plastic bottle filled with stones. You need one fewer pearls than there are players or 'divers'.

Throw the pearls into the pool. Each diver must find a pearl. The diver who doesn't find a pearl is out. Take one pearl away and begin the game again. Continue until you have one winning diver.

Remember to take out any remaining pearls from the pool after you have finished playing.

SPOT THE DIFFERENCE

There are 15 differences between the underwater scenes below.
Can you spot them? You can check your answers on page 63.

ISLAND DISCOVERY

Test your map-reading skills by studying the map below.
Can you answer the questions using the compass above to help you?
Check your answers on page 63.

1. What number is on the sailing boat to the northeast of the island?

2. How many round huts are located in the northwest of the island?

3. Is the giant head positioned in the east or west of the island?

4. What tall building is at the island's most southwesterly point?

5. What is immediately east of the six palm trees?

6. How many flags are there on the island?

Now see if any of your friends and family can do it from memory. Simply let them study the map for two minutes then cover it up and see how many questions they can answer correctly.

WHAT SHALL WE DO TODAY?

Get outside and have fun with these exciting outdoor activities.

SET UP AN ASSAULT COURSE

Set up the assault course below on the beach or on some grass.

Stick 3. Say the alphabet backwards, while rubbing your tummy and patting your head at the same time.

Stick 4. Throw a ball in the air and catch it, while hopping on one leg.

Place a stick in the ground and mark a Start/Finish line.

Then place another stick roughly 40 metres away from the first and three smaller sticks spaced evenly between the two.

All competitors must complete the following tasks at each stick:

Stick 1. Take off one shoe and do ten star jumps on the spot.

Stick 2. Drop to the floor and do five push-ups.

Now sprint back towards the start/finish line. Don't forget to stop and put your shoe back on before you cross the line.

Time how long each competitor takes to complete the course using the second hand on a watch. The fastest to reach the finish line wins.

GO CRABBING

If you are holidaying near a harbour or tidal river, why not go crab fishing?

You will need:

- a ball of string • a stick (roughly half a metre long) • a net • a fish hook and small weight (from a local fishing shop)
- a bucket • bacon pieces or scraps of fish from the fishmonger (for bait)

1. Head down to your crab-fishing location with the equipment above and an adult to share the fun with. Why not ask local people to recommend a good spot?

2. Tie one end of the string to your stick – the string needs to be long enough to reach from your stick to the bottom of the water.

3. Tie the weight onto the string near the end of your line. Tie the hook securely to the end of the string. Push the bait onto the hook.

4. Drop the baited line into the water and wait for a crab to take the bait – you will feel a firm tug on your string when you've got one.

5. Slowly lift your line out of the water and catch the crab in the net. Gently transfer your crab into your bucket filled with water.

Warning. Crabs are living creatures, so treat them gently and always put your crabs back where you caught them. Never keep crabs out of the sea for longer than a couple of hours. Never go crabbing without an adult.

SCRAPBOOK STICKING

Scrapbooks are great for jogging your memory – when you look back later, you'll remember all sorts of things about your trip.

To make a scrapbook of your holiday, hunt for the items listed in the boxes below. Each evening, you can have fun sticking them down in the spaces provided.

TICKETS FROM BUSES, TRAINS AND BOATS

CUT-OUTS FROM LEAFLETS OF PLACES YOU VISIT

A LEAF FROM A TREE NEAR WHERE YOU ARE STAYING

A MAP OF THE LOCAL AREA

SWEET WRAPPERS

A SMALL COIN FROM THE COUNTRY THAT YOU ARE IN

A CLEAN PAPER NAPKIN FROM A CAFÉ

BE A STONE-SKIMMING CHAMP

Hold a stone-skimming competition down at the water's edge – the first person to skim a stone that 'bounces' six times before going 'plop', wins.

HOW TO SKIM A STONE

1. Choose your stone well. A round, smooth, flat one, that is roughly the size of your palm and weighs about the same as an apple is best.

2. Find an area of calm water to practise your stone-skimming technique.

3. Stand side-on to the water, and crouch with your feet apart.

5. Sweep your arm back, then jerk it forward. Use your wrist and index finger to spin the stone as it leaves your hand.

4. Curl your index finger around the edge of the stone and place your thumb flat on top of it. Your middle finger should be flat underneath, to make sure the stone stays completely horizontal when you throw it.

Top Tip. The angle at which you throw the stone is very important. If the stone hits the water at an angle that is too steep, its edge will catch and it will sink. If the angle is too shallow, the stone will glide along without bouncing. Practise until you achieve a perfect skimmer.

MESSAGE IN A BOTTLE

You are strolling by the sea skimming stones, when all of a sudden you spy a plastic bottle. Then another, and then another. You notice that each bottle contains a rolled up piece of paper...

1. On the paper inside the first bottle, you find the following cryptic message:

'X L M T I Z G F O Z G R L M H! B L F S Z E V D L M Z U I V V R X V X I V Z N!'

Need a clue to decode it? Write the alphabet backwards under a normal alphabet and substitute each letter in the message for the letter below it. Can you work out what it says?

2. You look inside the second bottle and find this message:

K I V H V M G G S V H V

NVHHZTVH ZG QLV'H XZUV GL XOZRN...

Can you work out what it means?

3. The third bottle contains an even stranger-looking message. On the paper you find the grid below and this cryptic message:

'Colour in the squares you need, to show you something you can read.'

Can you crack the code?

All the answers on page 63.

2 4 7	A	E	G	E	L	A	R
1 3 6 7	A	S	G	S	O	A	L
2 5	F	K	H	O	E	M	E
1 3 6	F	M	L	A	D	B	E
1 4 5	M	L	E	U	A	M	O
2 3 5 6 7	N	E	F	A	W	M	L
1 3 4 6 7	A	D	A	A	E	A	H

GONE CAMPING

Have some fun at the camp site with these cool camping activities and puzzles.

BUILD A BASE CAMP

Why not make use of all the trees around you and create your very own camouflaged base camp?

You will need:

- a ball of string • scissors • a large bed sheet or groundsheet • three sturdy sticks roughly 1.5 m long
- one stick roughly 2 m long

1. Find a tree with a forked branch.

2. Take the three shorter sticks and tie them together with some string to form a tripod shape. Push the sticks into the ground at a 45 degree angle.

3. Place the longer stick on top of the tripod shape and secure with string.

Rest the other end of this stick in the fork of the tree, as shown above.

4. Carefully lay the sheeting over the frame. Secure it by placing heavy stones on the ends of the sheeting so that it doesn't blow away.

5. Cover your tent with wet leaves or mud to camouflage it.

TENT TROUBLE

To solve this puzzle you must add tents into the boxes on the grid, so that every tree has at least one tent horizontally or vertically next to it (but not diagonally).

Beside each row and below each column is a number that tells you how many tents they contain.

No tent can be in a next-door square to another tent (not even diagonally).

When every tree has a tent, and all the numbers are correct, you've cracked the tent teaser. Finally, check you have solved this puzzle correctly on page 63.

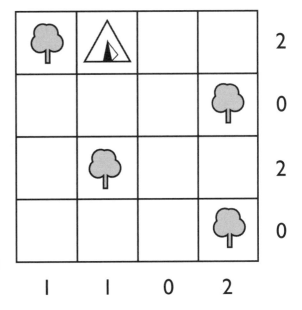

Now have a go at finding the tents in the larger grid below – this one is a bit harder, but it works in exactly the same way. We've started you off with the first tent. Can you find where the missing tents are? Check your answers on page 63.

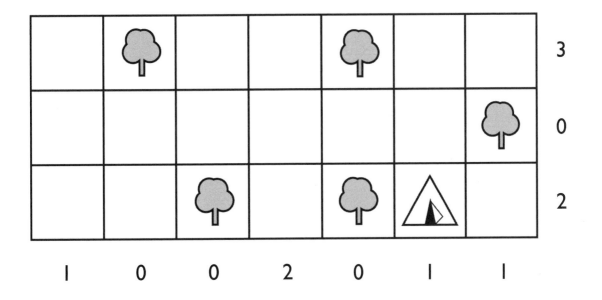

ROLLER-COASTER RIDE

Everybody loves a trip to the theme park.

If you can't have a go on a real roller coaster, have fun cracking these roller-coaster themed puzzles instead – you'll find all the answers on page 63.

STAR SPOTTING

Can you spot the 20 stars that are hiding on this picture?

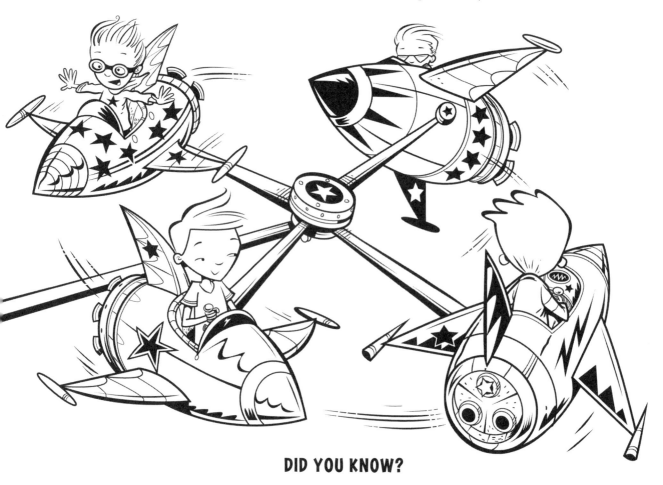

DID YOU KNOW?

Over 500 years ago, the Russians invented a slide that you could ride on – very much like a roller coaster. The structure came to be known as the Russian Ice Slides in which riders climbed up wooden stairs attached to a large slide that was covered in ice. They then slid down the slope of ice and were propelled up to the top of another slide. By the 1780s, millions of people had flocked to have a go on these sliding rides. It is believed these slides became the model for the modern roller coaster that you can see today.

COASTER CONUNDRUM

These four circles represent roller coasters that loop, twist, go upside down and go backwards.

Where the circles cross over each other, the coasters do more than one thing. For example, area J is for coasters that twist and go upside down, and area D is for coasters that go backwards and loop.

Can you work out what area is for coasters that twist and loop and go upside down, but do not go backwards?

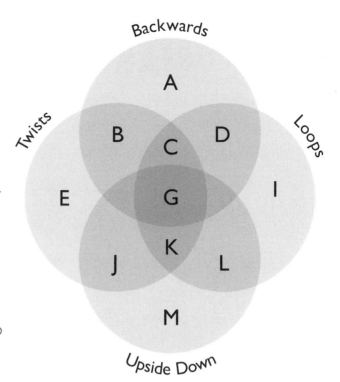

RON'S ON

Roller-coaster Ron loves to ride.

He doesn't wear headphones while riding.

He never wears zips or buttons.

Can you spot him?

MASTER BUILDER

Below is a picture of the Taj Mahal, a beautiful building in India. Every year, millions of tourists flock to admire it.

Using the squares in the grid below to help you, can you copy it?

WHAT KIND OF TRAVELLER ARE YOU?

Are you an amazing adventurer or a couch potato? Consider the following questions and see the next page to find out what your answers say about you as a traveller.

---

1. Where would you most like to go for a holiday?

A. The North Pole
B. A tropical beach
C. The Amazon Rainforest

---

2. Which of the following dishes would you choose to eat from this menu?

A. Crispy-fried locusts
B. Pizza
C. Ostrich steak

---

3. What do you always take with you on your travels?

A. A compass
B. Your MP3 player
C. A camera

---

4. Which of these activities would you like to do on a holiday?

A. Climb a glacier
B. Ride on a roller coaster
C. Fly in a hot-air balloon

---

5. Which form of transport would you prefer to use on holiday?

A. A dirt bike
B. A limousine
C. A local bus

---

6. Which item of clothing will you need most on your trip?

A. A crash helmet
B. A Hawaiian shirt
C. Walking boots

---

7. Which book will you take with you on your trip?

A. A book of survival tips
B. The latest crime thriller novel
C. A local guidebook

---

8. What sport might you want to take part in while you're away?

A. Hang-gliding
B. Frisbee
C. Football

---

9. What would you do if you got lost and couldn't find your way home?

A. Navigate your way by the stars
B. Call Mum
C. Ask someone for directions

---

10. Where will you sleep when you get there?

A. In a cave
B. In a luxury hotel
C. In a youth hostel

WHAT YOUR ANSWERS SAY ABOUT YOU ...

Count up how many times you answered A, B or C in the quiz on page 27. Read on, to reveal what your answers say about you. If you scored an even mix of letters, then you are a traveller who will enjoy whichever part of the globe you visit.

Mostly As

You are a born adventurer.

You are a true adventurer, scared of nothing and willing to throw yourself into any activity, no matter how dangerous it might appear to be. You will go far, possibly even to Mars! Have fun on your adventures, but take care.

Mostly Bs

You are a chilled-out traveller.

You like to chill out and play games on holiday. You know what you like and don't see much point in trying new things. You might not travel far from home, but you are pretty sure you'll enjoy yourself wherever you go.

Mostly Cs

You love to experience other cultures.

You are a born traveller. You are interested in people and in experiencing different places around the world. You will travel the world and make lots of friends.

DID YOU KNOW?

Read on, for some fascinating facts about the deep blue sea.
Your friends will be impressed with how much you learnt on holiday...

FACT. Water covers nearly 71% of the Earth's surface. The biggest areas of water are called oceans, and contain 97% of all the water in the world.

FACT. Every year the amount of rubbish dumped into the oceans is about three times heavier than the weight of the fish taken out of them.

FACT. The Pacific Ocean is the biggest in the world, occupying nearly a third of the whole surface of the Earth.

FACT. Coral reefs are made from millions of soft, tube-shaped creatures that produce hard calcium deposits – like bones – that they live in. Over thousands of years, these can grow into massive structures.

The Great Barrier Reef is a coral reef found in the Pacific Ocean off the northeast coast of Australia. It is over 2,000 km long and covers an area larger than the size of the UK – it can even be seen from space.

FACT. The giant Pacific octopus is the largest octopus in the octopus species, growing to an average of 5 metres long and weighing around 50 kg.

The pigment in their cells can change colour, allowing them to blend into their surroundings and hide them from predators.

Using their sharp, beak-like mouths, they can even attack and eat sharks!

WORLD RALLY

Start your engines, it's time to race!

Each player must place a coin on the start line. Take it in turns to spin the spinner and move your coin. You must follow the instructions on the square that you land on. The first person to race around three laps, wins.

STAR DRIVER! Have another spin.

NO PETROL Go to the petrol station to fill up and miss a turn.

PETROL

TURBO BOOST Move forward 4 squares.

SHORT CUT Cut through here.

CRASH! Go back and start the lap again.

PITS

START AND FINISH ➡

PIT STOP!
Go in to the pits and miss a turn.

TURBO BOOST
Move forward 2 squares.

GARAGE

DRIVER!
Have another spin.

BREAKDOWN
Go to the garage and miss 2 turns.

SPINNER

To spin your spinner, hold a toothpick upright with one hand, and spin the spinner with the other. The number that is at the top of the spinner when it stops tells you the number of spaces you should move.

Complete the battle on board!

BACK OF SPINNER

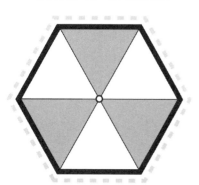

THE LEGEND OF BLACKBEARD

Of all the pirates who ever lived, perhaps the most feared was 'Blackbeard'.
Read all about his pirating misadventures below.

Captain Blackbeard was born in Bristol, England, in around 1680. His real name remains uncertain – either Edward Drummond or Edward Teach, no one is sure. When he grew up, he left Bristol and headed for the island of Jamaica in the Caribbean. There he joined the crew of Benjamin Hornigold, a pirate captain, who taught him how to ambush ships and steal their cargoes.

Together, they ambushed a ship and took it for themselves. Arming it with 40 cannons, they named it *The Queen Anne's Revenge*. Blackbeard soon became captain of this ship, with his own fearsome crew.

Blackbeard got his name because before an attack he would tie his beard together with black ribbons. He then stuffed rope under his pirate hat and set it alight, making him look very scary indeed!

His most famous mission was a raid on a port on the East Coast of America in 1718. Blackbeard stole the cargo of five ships, taking several people hostage in the process. He escaped with a mighty stash of booty, but not before releasing the hostages unharmed – without their clothes!

Blackbeard hoped to retire rich after this raid, but two American captains, named Maynard and Hyde, had other ideas. They both went off in pursuit of the troublesome pirate.

They finally found him on the morning of November 22nd, 1718. A bloody battle took place, with Hyde and six of his men killed in an attack from Blackbeard's cannons.

Blackbeard died that day from pistol and cutlass wounds. Maynard sailed away from the bloody scene triumphant, with the pirate captain's severed head hanging from the bow of his ship.

MAKE YOUR OWN TREASURE MAP

Beaches are great places for burying stuff, as any good pirate knows, and a pirate who wants to stash his booty needs to make a map so he can find it again.

BURY YOUR TREASURE

Bury your treasure – a chocolate bar that's completely sealed to keep out the sand is perfect.

Mark the spot with a stick until you have made your map.

WHICH WAY IS NORTH?

First you need to work out which is north. To do this, move your body so you are facing the sun. In the morning, the sun is in the east, and in the afternoon the sun is in the west.

Stretch your arms out to your sides and turn your body so that your left arm is pointing west and your right arm is pointing east. The direction your nose is pointing in is north.

Choose an object that won't move, such as a tree. Starting at the tree, walk towards your treasure, counting your paces (make sure your paces are all roughly the same size). If you have to change direction to avoid something, write down the number of paces you have made, note down the new direction you have to walk in, and start counting from one again.

MAP-MAKING

On a piece of paper, mark your treasure with an 'X' and mark the tree. Draw a line from the treasure to the tree.

Now write out the directions from the tree. For example:

*From the tree, take 12 paces north,
5 paces east, 3 paces north,
6 paces west and 10 paces south.
X marks the spot where
my treasure is buried!*

Remove the stick that marks your treasure and smooth the sand over it so the treasure is well hidden.

Hand the map to your friends and see if they can find your treasure.

TREASURE HUNT

Blackbeard's treasure map has been found.

He has buried two cutlasses, two amulets, two keys and two bars of Spanish silver, and their location is shown in this grid map. He forgot to mark where the cutlasses are and where he has hidden the missing key. Can you find them in the grid map below? See if you have located them correctly on page 63.

HOW TO PLAY

1. The numbers beside each row and under each column tell you how many squares in that row or that column are occupied. For example, the top row has the numbers 1 and 2 by it, which tells you that 3 squares are occupied – one square on its own and then two squares right next to each other.

2. You can see where the two amulets are, both bars of silver and one of the keys that have been buried. Can you work out where the two cutlasses and the missing key are hidden?

Top Tip. Start by putting an 'X' in squares that you know are occupied, and an 'O' in squares you know are empty. When you have an 'X' or an 'O' in each of the squares, you should be able to work out what lies buried beneath them.

THE TREASURE

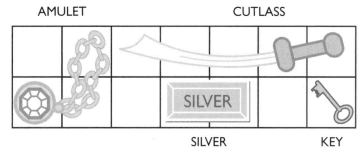

AMULET   CUTLASS
SILVER   KEY

THE GRID MAP

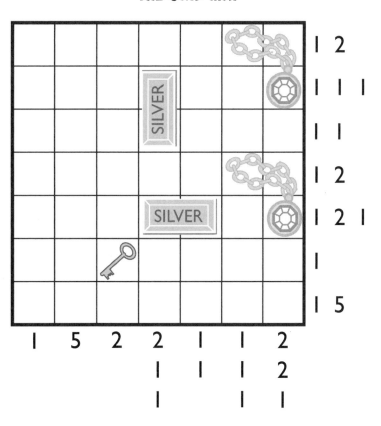

THE ROCK-POOLING GAME

This is a scavenger hunt you can play by the sea. Rock pools can be home to lots of creatures and plants... all you have to do is find them.

SCAVENGER HUNT

1. Head down to the beach with your family and find an area where there are lots of rock pools.

2. The aim of the game is to spot each item that is on the checklist below. Write the initials of the person that spots it first in the box next to the item.

3. The winner is the person who spots the most items on the checklist.

Top Tip. Carefully lift up rocks in and around rock pools – you will often find little creatures hiding there.

CHECKLIST

1. A barnacle

2. A white shell

3. A sea anemone

4. A bivalve (a shell with two halves)

5. Brown seaweed

6. A stone with a stripe

7. A crab

8. A fish

9. A pink shell

10. A shrimp

Fill the ferry with cars.

WHIRLYBIRD HELICOPTERS

Whirlybirds are paper helicopters – throw them up in the air or drop them from a height and they'll twirl slowly downwards like helicopters coming in to land. They're easy to make, fun to decorate and great to play with.

Follow the instructions on the opposite page to make your whirlybirds.

To throw your whirlybird, hold it by the paper clip and lob it in the air – if you have made it correctly, it should spin all the way back to the ground.

A simple game to play with a friend is to throw your whirlybirds up in the air at the same time. The one that hits the ground last, wins.

Alternatively, you could play the Target Game.

THE TARGET GAME

You need to make a 'target' by drawing two circles, one inside the other, on a piece of paper. To do this, place a dinner plate on a piece of paper and draw around it. Place a side plate in the centre and draw around it to form an inner circle. Cut around the outer circle. Now place your target on the ground.

You can play this game with as many people as you want. Players throw their whirlybirds up in the air at the same time and see whose lands closest to the centre of the target. Score one point if your whirlybird lands touching the outer circle and three points if it lands touching the inner circle. The player with the most points after six rounds, wins the game.

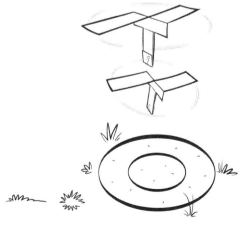

A	B
C	D

MAKING A WHIRLYBIRD

You will need:

- a sheet of paper • pens
- paperclips • a pair of scissors

1. Draw the pattern opposite onto the sheet of paper and cut it out. Decorate it using pens (or crayons) to make your whirlybird stand out from the crowd.

2. Using scissors, carefully cut along the solid lines of the pattern.

3. Fold section A forward and fold section B back, so that they now are suspended at a 90 degree angle to the rest of the paper.

4. Fold along the dotted lines of pieces C and D, folding one forward and one back. Press them together to make a three-layered sandwich in the middle.

5. Fold the flap up from the bottom – it doesn't matter which way – and secure with a paperclip. This will add a little weight to the bottom of the whirlybird that will help it fall to the ground more easily.

Top Tip. Add extra paperclips to the flap at the bottom of your whirlybird to make it spin to the ground faster.

ROAD TRIP

Have you ever imagined taking a road trip in the car of your dreams?
If so, you'll enjoy being behind the wheel on this puzzle adventure.

AMERICAN ADVENTURE

You've decided to take a road trip around America. You're going to make three separate car journeys, and one aeroplane flight. Can you work out which cities you will pass through on each trip described below? Now write down which three cities you will not visit because you don't pass through the squares in which they appear. The answers are on page 64.

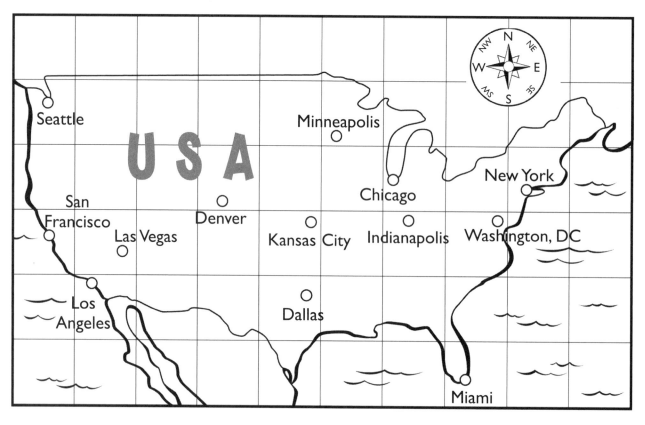

Trip A. From New York, you drive one square west, then three squares south, then one square north, then six squares west.

Trip B. You fly to Seattle. From there you drive five squares east, then one square south, then one square east, then 5 squares west, then one square south.

Trip C. From Las Vegas, you drive one square south, then six squares east, then two squares north and one square east.

Design the car you would drive on a road trip.

PUZZLE CITY

The city never sleeps and neither will you with these puzzles keeping you awake. All the answers are on page 64.

CAPITAL CITY CHECKLIST

Match the capital cities to the countries in which they are found. The first one has been done for you to get you started.

Bangkok — Thailand
New Delhi — India
Beijing — China
Madrid — Spain
Moscow — Russia
Berlin — Germany
Paris — France
Washington, DC — USA
Canberra — Australia

ROUND THE BLOCK

Follow the directions below and see where you would end up.

Turn right out of garage A and take the first right. Turn right again, then take the first left. Take the second right, then turn left and then take the first left.

Which garage do you end up in, B or C?

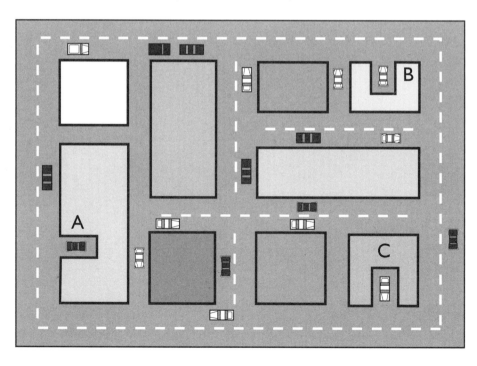

RAINY DAY GAMES

If it's too wet to play outside, why not have a go at these finger-flicking indoor ball games?

TABLE-TOP FOOTBALL

1. Find three coins, a table and someone to play with.

2. Sit opposite each other. Player A makes a goal by placing his fist against the edge of the table, with his first and fourth fingers stretched out on top.

3. Player B positions the three coins in a triangle – one coin behind the other two. He then flicks the back coin with his finger, attempting to shoot it between the front two coins and into the goal.

4. If Player B scores a goal, fails to shoot his coin between the front two coins, or if he blasts his coin off the table, it is Player A's turn to have a go.

First to score five goals, wins the game.

INDOOR CRAZY GOLF

1. Find some paper, empty loo rolls, a few books and someone to play with.

2. Scrunch up nine balls of paper tightly – these will be your 'hole balls'. Place the hole balls on the floor around the room and position the empty loo rolls and books between them.

3. Make a 'golf ball' by scrunching up another sheet of paper.

4. Take it in turns to flick the golf ball so that it passes around or through the obstacles and hits each of the hole balls.

Record how many flicks it takes each player to hit each hole ball on the course. The player who completes the course in the lowest number of flicks, wins.

CARS, PLANES AND TRAINS

Kick-start your brain into gear with these perplexing puzzles.
Check your answers on page 64.

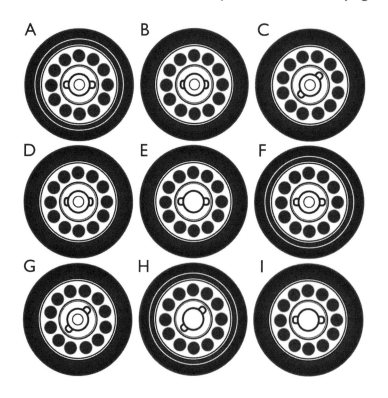

WHICH WHEELS?

These nine wheels look very similar, but in fact there are four matching pairs and one wheel which is not like any other.

Can you pick out the four pairs and spot the wheel that is the odd one out?

BITS 'N' PIECES

Only one of the boxes below contains all the bits needed to make this picture of a plane.

Can you work out which box it is?

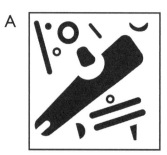

TRAIN TRACKER

The three squares below all appear in the main picture of the train. See if you can track them all down. Once you have found each square, write down its co-ordinates – this is the exact location of the square in the grid. To write down the co-ordinates of a square, simply write down the letter of the row and the number of the column in which it appears.

BODYBOARD LIKE A PRO

Bodyboarding is lots of fun and easier to master than standing up on a surfboard, so what are you waiting for? Get your hands on a bodyboard and learn how it's done below – you'll be catching waves in no time.

GETTING STARTED

You will need a bodyboard – a cheap foam one from a shop near the beach will do.

If your bodyboard has a leash, attach it to your wrist. Your leash attaches you to the board, so that when you fall off, you won't lose your board.

Wear a thick T-shirt – this will protect your chest and stomach from getting grazed by the board.

Swim fins (mini flippers) will help you paddle harder, and catch a wave.

PADDLING OUT

1. Walk into the sea, holding your board under your arm. When you are waist-deep, hold the board in front of you so that it is floating on top of the water.

2. Lean your whole body forward onto the board so that your belly is resting on the bottom end and your feet are behind you near the surface of the water.

3. Move yourself along by scooping water with your hands and kicking hard with your feet. Paddle out in this way to where the waves are just beginning to break. Wait here until you can see a wave that you want to ride.

CATCHING A WAVE

4. When you see a wave that you want to catch, turn your whole body so that you and your board are facing the beach. Put both of your hands at the top of the board, and grip the edges tightly.

5. Wait for the wave to come up behind you and then start kicking.

Kick as
hard as you
can until you feel the
wave start to carry you along.

6. Once the wave is moving you along in the water, turn your body and board to the left, so that you are travelling along the front of the wave.

7. Place your left hand at the top of the board and move your right hand down to the side of it.

8. Pull your body forward over the front of the board. Lift your head up high by arching your back and get your feet and fins out of the water. Hold on tight!

9. Lean your weight into the wave, and pull the board upwards with your right hand – this will dig the opposite side of the board into the wave and stop you sliding down it.

10. By pulling up, or relaxing your grip on the right side of the board, you can make yourself go up or down the front of the wave, and build up speed.

With a bit of luck, you will catch a wave and have the ride of your life.

Warning. Never go in the sea alone. Only get in the water if you can see a red and yellow flag flying on the beach – this means that there is a trained lifeguard on the beach.

HOLIDAY BINGO

Holiday Bingo is a great game, perfect for three players.

Two of the players are trying to make space in their rucksacks, and one is calling out the items they can get rid of. The first to lose all their items shouts BINGO! and wins the game.

HOW TO PLAY

1. Choose who is going to be the 'Caller' first. The other two players will be the 'Travellers'.

2. With a pair of scissors, cut out the rucksacks on the page opposite, and each of the item counters.

3. The two Travellers then pick who plays with the 'dog counters' and 'dog rucksack', and who plays with the 'cat counters' and 'cat rucksack', (see page 50).

4. Without letting the Caller see, the Travellers must choose six counters and put them in their rucksack game-board, face up.

The Travellers must keep their boards hidden from the Caller, at all times.

5. The Caller now calls out the name of an item from the list below, for example, 'Take out the headphones'. If either or both Travellers have the headphones in their rucksacks, they then hand it to the Caller.

6. The Caller carries on naming random items from the list below in any order he likes, until one of the Travellers has emptied his rucksack.

7. The first Traveller to lose all his items from his rucksack shouts BINGO!

LIST OF ITEMS

1. Shorts	7. Spade
2. Baseball cap	8. Bucket
3. Postcard	9. Sunglasses
4. Flip-Flops	10. Beach Ball
5. Hawaiian shirt	11. Camera
6. Headphones	12. Coin

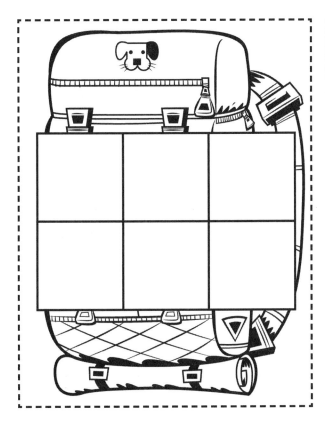

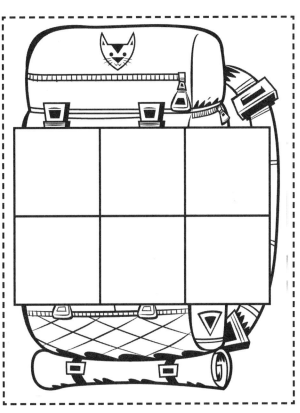

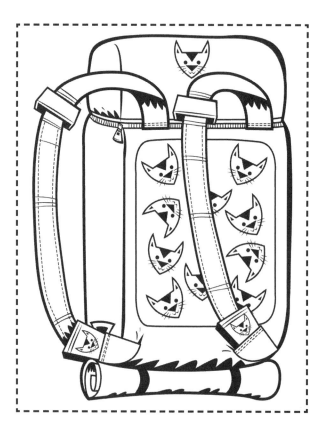

WATER WORLD

Can you work out which two water-skiers
have lost their boats? Check your answers on page 64.

SUMMER SPORTS

Make the most of a sunny day and bring
family and friends together in a serious sporting showdown.
Here are two perfect games to play on a summer's afternoon.

ULTIMATE FRISBEE

1. Draw your pitch in the sand or mark it out on grass, as shown below. If you don't have enough space simply use the space available.

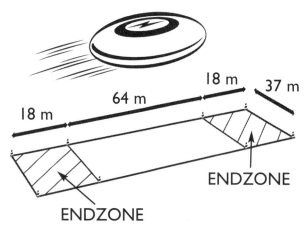

18 m

64 m

18 m

37 m

ENDZONE

ENDZONE

Place buckets or jumpers on the ground to mark the scoring areas, or 'endzones'.

2. Split into two equal teams (at least seven players per team is ideal).

3. Each team lines up in their endzone. To start, the team with the Frisbee tosses it to a member of the opposition. Only then can players leave their endzone.

At least one of each team must remain in their endzone at all times to act as defence. Other players can move anywhere, including the other endzone.

4. To score a point, players must pass the Frisbee to a member of your team who is standing in the other team's endzone. After each point, teams swap ends.

5. Play passes to the other team if:

- A player doesn't pass the Frisbee within ten seconds of catching it.
- A player runs with the Frisbee.
- A player throws the Frisbee out of the pitch, or the Frisbee hits the ground.

The winning team is the one with most points after 20 minutes.

Go for it!

FRENCH CRICKET

1. Grab a bouncy tennis ball and a bat. A cricket bat is ideal, but a rounders bat, a softball bat, a tennis racket or even a plastic spade will do.

2. Decide who is going to bat first. The batsman stands with his feet together, holding the bat in front of his legs.

3. All the other players are 'fielders'. One fielder bowls the ball underarm, trying to hit the batsman on the legs, below his knees.

4. The batsman must protect his legs with his bat and hit the ball away.

5. The fielders must try to catch or stop the ball as quickly as possible, and bowl it at the batsman from the spot on which they stopped the ball.

6. The batsman turns to face each new bowler and protects his legs again.

7. If the batsman misses a ball, but it doesn't hit his legs, he can't move his feet to face the next bowler. He can only twist his body round and do his best to protect his legs.

8. The batsman scores one point for each ball he hits. If a fielder catches the ball after he has hit it and before it bounces on the ground, the batsman's turn is over. If the ball hits the batsman's legs below his knees, his turn is over and the bat is passed to another player.

9. The player with the most points after each player has taken a turn, wins.

Can you add more fielders in this game?

DOWN ON THE FARM

Get your wellies on and prepare to get mucky down on the farm.
See page 64 for the answers.

ANIMALS EVERYWHERE

If you take a trip to a farm you'll find creatures you rarely see in the city.
There are 20 animals and birds in this picture – can you find them all?

JOIN THE DOTS

Join up the dots in the correct order to find out what this boy is feeding.

FIELD WORK

Farmer Brown has four sheep and four pigs in his field.

Can you draw two straight lines across the field to divide it into four areas? Each area must have one sheep and one pig in it.

MAKE A MINI KITE

Make one of these super-light mini kites and take it for a spin on a blustery day – be sure to hold on tight!

WHAT YOU DO

You will need:

- two sheets of tissue paper
- two straight drinking straws
- 3 m of cotton thread
- PVA glue • scissors • a pen

1. Place a sheet of tissue paper over the pattern on the page opposite and trace around it with your pen. Using scissors, carefully cut around the kite shape and the fin shape.

2. Cut the straws to make them the right length to fit across the kite in a cross shape. Glue them down, as shown. Leave to dry.

3. To attach the fin, fold the strip along the dotted line. Glue it down the middle of your kite, on the opposite side to the straws.

4. Cut two strips of tissue paper – roughly 2 cms by 12 cm. These will be your kite's tails. Glue one end of each tail to the bottom of the kite on the same side as the fin. Leave to dry.

5. Glue the end of a 3-m length of thread to the fin, in the area that is indicated. Leave to dry completely.

FLY, FLY, FLY!

On a windy day, take your kite outside – somewhere where you have a large open space.

Holding the end of the string firmly in your hands, ask a friend to hold the kite above his head until the wind takes it. When your kite is in the air, avoid pulling hard on the thread – keep all your movements smooth and gentle and see how high your kite can fly.

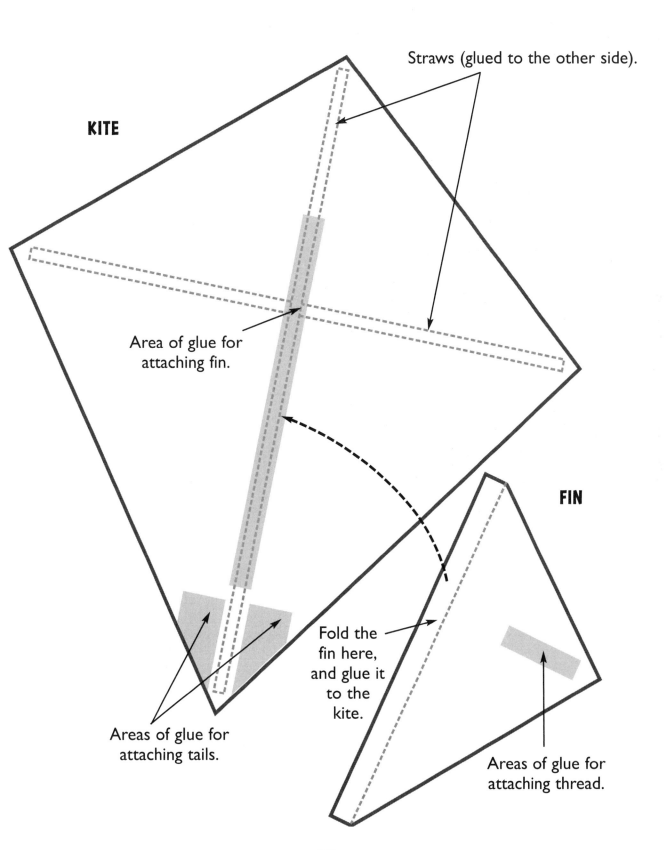

Straws (glued to the other side).

KITE

Area of glue for
attaching fin.

FIN

Fold the
fin here,
and glue it
to the
kite.

Areas of glue for
attaching tails.

Areas of glue for
attaching thread.

SPOOKY STORY

Sitting around a campfire sharing spooky stories is great fun.
Here are some story-telling tips and a story to give everyone the creeps.

STORY-TELLING TIPS

1. Point a torch under your chin shining upwards to make your face look eerie.

2. Pretend the tale you are about to tell is a true story and that you read it in a magazine somewhere ...

3. Keep your voice quiet so everyone has to lean forwards to hear you.

4. When you get to the scary ending, leave a long pause before you deliver it. Say the last words much LOUDER.

A TRUE STORY

Grandpa Henry had been dead for a couple of years, and his grandson, Ben, missed him very much. Grandpa was buried in the cemetery next to Ben's house, and Ben could see the grave from his bedroom window.

One night, Ben dreamt he woke to find himself alone in the house. His parents were nowhere to be found. A storm raged outside. The wind howled, and broken branches crashed across the garden.

Suddenly the phone rang. Ben picked it up... it was the voice of Grandpa!

'Don't be scared Ben, you're having a dream. You will wake up soon', said Grandpa's voice.

Suddenly Ben woke up. He peered out of his window and saw that there had in fact been a real storm and the grass was strewn with fallen branches. He saw that the telephone line to the house had broken and the wire hung down right over Grandpa Henry's grave ...

Ben turned from the window, thinking what a strange coincidence it was. At that moment, he heard a noise... it was the noise of the PHONE RINGING!

BUILD A SAND-CASTLE FORT

To make the most impressive sand castle on the beach,
follow the tips below.

1. Choose an area quite close to the sea so you don't have to walk miles to fetch water. Mark out a big square with a stick, and pour water over it to make the sand firm.

2. Pile a mound of sand on top of the square area. Pour water all over it and pat it firmly down with your spade. This will give you a solid base to build your castle on.

3. Fill a bucket with sand, pat the sand in firmly, then turn the bucket over to produce the main body of a tower.

4. To make the turret at the top, shape a thick disk of wet sand and gently flatten it with the palm of your hand.

Place a smaller disk on top, and another smaller disk on top, making a cone shape. Smooth out the sides of your turret.

5. Make four towers, as shown below, and connect them with strong walls of damp sand. Make the walls thicker at the bottom so they won't fall over.

6. Make a door in your walls by gently tunnelling in at the bottom, scraping out sand gradually with your finger until you have carved an arched entrance.

7. Dig a moat around the base of your castle. Leave a bridge across it to the door and wait for the sea to come in and fill up the moat.

Top Tip. Using your finger, carve the outline of bricks on your castle walls.

DOODLE ALBUM

Make your own doodle album – simply draw or paint all the exciting things you did on holiday in the spaces below.

CHECK YOUR ANSWERS

UP, UP AND AWAY
pages 6 and 7

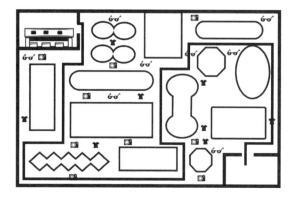

PICTURE PUZZLER
page 10

WORD FACTS QUIZ
page 8

1. C	6. A	11. A
2. B	7. A	12. B
3. D	8. D	13. C
4. C	9. D	14. C
5. D	10. A	

WORLD SPORTING CHALLENGE
page 11

Cristiano Ronaldo – Football – Portugal
Lewis Hamilton – Motor racing – Great Britain
Roger Federer – Tennis – Switzerland
Tiger Woods – Golf – USA
Sachin Tendulkar – Cricket – India
Usain Bolt – Athletics – Jamaica
Ian Thorpe – Swimming – Australia

SPOT THE DIFFERENCE
page 14

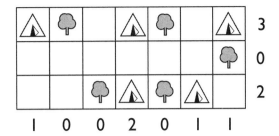

ROLLER-COASTER RIDE
pages 24 and 25

Area K is for coasters that twist and loop and go upside down, but not backwards.

Ron is the man with the beard in the second row.

ISLAND DISCOVERY
page 15

1. 12
2. 5
3. West
4. A lighthouse
5. A swimming pool
6. 6

MESSAGE IN A BOTTLE
page 21

1. Message reads: 'Congratulations! You have won a free ice cream!'

2. The alphabet is spelt out backwards again. The decoded message spells out: 'Present these messages at Joe's Café to claim...'

3. Colour in the squares matching the numbers by each row. The letters left spell out: 'A glass of home-made lemonade'.

TENT TROUBLE
page 23

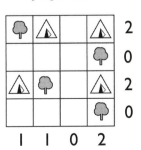

TREASURE HUNT
page 35

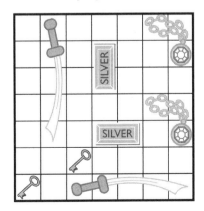

AMERICAN ADVENTURE
page 40

Trip A. New York, Washington, DC, Miami, Dallas. Los Angeles.

Trip B. Seattle, Minneapolis, Chicago, Denver, Las Vegas.

Trip C. Las Vegas, Los Angeles, Dallas, Washington, DC, New York.

You have not visited San Francisco, Kansas City or Indianapolis.

PUZZLE CITY
page 42

Bangkok = Thailand

New Delhi = India

Beijing = China

Madrid = Spain

Moscow = Russia

Berlin = Germany

Paris = France

Washington, DC = USA

Canberra = Australia

You would end up in garage C.

CARS, PLANES AND TRAINS
pages 44 and 45

Wheels C and G, B and D, E and I, and A and F are the same.
Wheel H is unique.

Kit B contains all the bits to build the plane.

The pieces match the following squares: H8, B4 and J2.

WATER WORLD
page 51

Skiers A and C have lost their boats.

DOWN ON THE FARM
pages 54 and 55

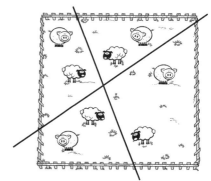

64